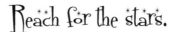

Reach for the stars.

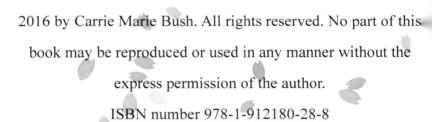

ISBN number 978-1-912180-28-8

E book ISBN number 978-1-912180-29-5

Design by Steve Swinden, 2016 (sswinden53@gmail.com)

Illustrated by Cintia Sand.

Printed by Createspace.

Archangel Jeremiel Helps with Anxiety

Carrie M Bush

Feathers will find you always

when I'm near

Sometimes a rainbow will appear

A star may twinkle

Some glitter may sprinkle

Music may play

All to show you I'm with you

each day

Archangel Jeremiel Helps with Anxiety

Tom had suffered with anxiety and panic attacks for a while now; he wasn't sure when or how they had started, but it seemed to be happening a lot lately! Some days were better than others, and some days it felt as though he was living under a big dark cloud.

Archangel Jeremiel Helps with Anxiety

He did not understand what triggered

the anxiety attacks. Boom! They would

suddenly appear. He would start to feel

warmth rise up from his feet, then his whole

body would become very hot.

Archangel Jeremiel Helps with Anxiety

His hands would get sweaty and he could hear his heart start to beat louder, like a drum!

It was a very scary feeling, and Tom hated it.

Tom's granddad had helped him feel better

by explaining that he had also suffered from

anxiety when he was a young boy.

He told him how his own mother had always

told him, "It's because you have a beautiful

mind that is so powerful that it thinks of so

many important things!"

Archangel Jeremiel Helps with Anxiety

That had made Tom giggle! But it also did make some sense to him. Tom's granddad said when he felt anxious he should place the palm of his hand on his tummy and breathe very slowly, but deeply; this would help him to stay calm. This did help Tom, but it didn't make the anxiety go away completely.

Archangel Jeremiel Helps with Anxiety

Tom and his granddad decided to go for a walk to the woods one day.

They put the lead onto Barney who got excited; his tail was wagging because he was a dog who loved his walks.

Archangel Jeremiel Helps with Anxiety

Archangel Jeremiel Helps with Anxiety

When they reached the woods, Tom and his granddad began to talk some more about anxiety. His granddad told him how walking in nature always helped him to get over his panic attacks. "You just have to walk and breathe this all in; all this natural beauty, Tom. You have to really look around you and see how amazing life is… It's very grounding for your body to be in nature."

Tom smiled. He loved how his granddad

always had such an amazing way with

words, and how he could always be relied on

to make him feel better.

Archangel Jeremiel Helps with Anxiety

"Granddad, how did you stop your anxiety

for good?" Tom asked.

"Well, there is a very magical story to that,"

his granddad replied with a wink!

Archangel Jeremiel Helps with Anxiety

Archangel Jeremiel Helps with Anxiety

He told Tom how his panic attacks become

so bad that his mum had held him close

one day and told him all about a powerful

archangel named Jeremiel.

She told him how he was the angel who

could help with positive changes and take

away worry and fear about the future ahead.

Archangel Jeremiel Helps with Anxiety

27

She explained that he worked best with

people by coming into their dreams and

giving them messages or just an idea.

He said how his mother had then made him

a dream catcher to hang above his bed.

Archangel Jeremiel Helps with Anxiety

It was a dark purple dream catcher, and she had made it this colour because this was Archangel Jeremiel's colour.

"She told me the dream catcher would catch all my bad dreams and only let the good ones come in, and then, if I asked at bedtime for the angel to help me, he would."

"Wow, granddad," Tom said, "That's amazing! Did it work straight away?"

"Yes, it did, Tom," his granddad replied with a big smile.

"I went to bed that night and I asked the angel to help me, just like my mother had told me. I lay just watching the purple dream catcher making patterns all around my bedroom, and when I woke up in the morning I could not believe it!

Archangel Jeremiel Helps with Anxiety

I had had a dream, and Archangel Jeremiel was in it; he had a long purple robe on, and he was surrounded with purple sparkles.

Archangel Jeremiel Helps with Anxiety

He told me that any time I felt anxious I must think of a purple beach with flowing purple water, and I must keep looking at the water gently flowing backwards and forwards until I was relaxed and calm again.

He also told me to find a dandelion with seeds on, and blow them away. They could be seen as my worries and fears blowing away in the wind.

Tom stood, shocked. "Granddad, that is amazing! Did you do it?"

"Yes," his granddad replied. "That very morning I found a dandelion with seeds and I blew hard, it felt good - as if I had blown all my worries up to heaven. I could feel Archangel Jeremiel catching them and smiling!

Archangel Jeremiel Helps with Anxiety

And then, after that day I only felt anxious once, and I thought about the purple water and I felt calm. The anxiety just went away!"

As Tom and his granddad started to make their way home, his granddad grabbed Tom's hand. "I think it's time I passed the purple dream catcher to you." He looked at Tom and smiled. "I always keep it at home." Later that day, Tom hung the purple dream catcher above his bed. "Perfect," his granddad said, "and remember, Tom, what my mother told me. When you suffer from anxiety, it is often an amazing mind packed full of brilliant ideas just waiting to come out and do wonderful things!"

Tom looked at his granddad and he felt happy.

'Thank you very much, Granddad. I'm excited

o go to bed!"

The next day when Tom saw his granddad, he couldn't wait to tell him that he had had a dream. "Granddad, it was amazing. Everything was purple, and the sky was full of balloons; they were floating everywhere!"

"Wow, Tom," his granddad said. "I think this means that you must release your fears and worries up to heaven in a balloon!"

Archangel Jeremiel Helps with Anxiety

Later that day, Tom, his granddad and Barney made their way back to the woods, this time with a purple balloon with a little note attached to it that Tom had written. It said, 'Archangel Jeremiel, I release all my worries.' They both stood silently, watching the balloon float high into the sky as it gently flew higher and higher. It was almost out of sight when Tom's granddad squeezed his hand gently. He whispered to Tom, "Here's to a fresh start and lots more magical dreams."

Archangel Jeremiel Helps with Anxiety

My angel wishes

1 _____

2 _____

3 _____

4 _____

5 _____

My angel wishes

6

7

If you enjoyed this book - you may also like:

Archangel Gabriel and the Dancer's Dream

Archangel Ariel Heals a Bird

Archangel Raguel Brings Harmony

Mia's Healing with Archangel Raphael

Archangel Metatron - The Fiery Angel

Archangel Raziel's Rainbow Bubble

Archangel Chamuel and the Lost Wish Box

Archangel Jophiel's Gift of Beauty and Joy

Archangel Haniel Brings Happiness

Archangel Azrael - Molly's Angel

Archangel Michael Saves the Day

Archangel Uriel Heals Eczema

Archangel Sandalphon's Magical Help

Willow Forgives with Archangel Zadkiel

For more information follow me on:

Twitter - @carriembush77
Facebook - https://m.facebook.com/CarrieMBush
Instagram - carriemariebush

May all your wishes come true...

24257485R00028

Printed in Great Britain
by Amazon